The Mother Chimpanzee

by Edith Thacher Hurd

Illustrated by Clement Hurd

Boston   Little, Brown and Company   Toronto

MANHASSET PUBLIC LIBRARY

Books in the Mother Animal Series

THE MOTHER BEAVER
THE MOTHER DEER
THE MOTHER WHALE
THE MOTHER OWL
THE MOTHER KANGAROO
THE MOTHER CHIMPANZEE

ILLUSTRATIONS COPYRIGHT © 1978 BY CLEMENT HURD

TEXT COPYRIGHT © 1978 BY EDITH THACHER HURD

ALL RIGHTS RESERVED. NO PART OF THIS BOOK MAY BE REPRODUCED IN ANY FORM
OR BY ANY ELECTRONIC OR MECHANICAL MEANS INCLUDING INFORMATION STOR-
AGE AND RETRIEVAL SYSTEMS WITHOUT PERMISSION IN WRITING FROM THE PUB-
LISHER, EXCEPT BY A REVIEWER WHO MAY QUOTE BRIEF PASSAGES IN A REVIEW.

FIRST EDITION

T 03/78

Library of Congress Cataloging in Publication Data

Hurd, Edith Thacher, 1910-
    The mother chimpanzee.

    (Mother animal series)
    SUMMARY: Describes the relationship of a mother and
baby chimpanzee.
    1. Chimpanzees — Behavior — Juvenile literature.
    2. Parental behavior in animals — Juvenile literature.
    3. Animals, Infancy of — Juvenile literature. [1. Chim-
panzees — Habits and behavior] I. Hurd, Clement,
1908- II. Title.
QL737.P96H87   599'.884   77-24747
ISBN 0-316-38327-9

Published simultaneously in Canada
by Little, Brown & Company (Canada) Limited

PRINTED IN THE UNITED STATES OF AMERICA

To Jane Goodall
with our grateful thanks

If she had not brought the life
of the chimpanzee into our lives
with so much interest and knowledge,
this book could not have been written.

Two young chimpanzees looked through the green leaves of the forest. Then they walked slowly toward the mother chimpanzee. They wanted to see their new baby sister.

The baby's face was all
wrinkles. She had two little
dark eyes. Her ears stood
out from the hair that grew
like a cap on her head.

The baby made a crying noise and reached out with her little fingers. The mother chimpanzee lifted her gently. The new baby was hungry and drank milk from her mother.

Now the dark night was coming and the mother chimpanzee wanted a safe nest for herself and her baby to sleep in. Holding the little chimpanzee close to her, she climbed a tall tree.

When she was almost at the top she pulled down two large branches. She put one on top of the other and held them with her feet. When the nest was big enough and strong enough, she covered it with smaller branches and leaves to make it soft for her new baby.

In the morning the warm sun woke the baby. She cried and drank milk from her mother. The mother chimpanzee was hungry too, but as she climbed from the nest she saw a huge male chimpanzee eating figs in a tree close by.

The male swung down from the tree and stood swaying in front of the mother chimpanzee. He gave a low bark and raised his hands over her head, but he did not hurt her. He only wanted to show her that she must not come too close to him when he was feeding.

11

The male patted the baby with his big hand. The mother chimpanzee had mated with many of the males in the group, but the male chimpanzees did not feed or help care for the babies or the young chimpanzees. The males lived by themselves or with the other males of the group. Sometimes they played with the babies, tickling or kissing them, or even grooming them when they were little.

When the big chimpanzee touched her baby so gently, the mother knew that he would not hurt her. She sat behind him and groomed him until she had combed out all of the leaves, dirt, and dry hair. At last the male went off into the forest and the mother climbed the fig tree.

Now the mother was thirsty. She crumpled a few leaves and pushed them into a hole in a tree where a little rainwater had collected. Then she chewed and sucked on the wet leaves.

By the time the baby chimpanzee was a few weeks old she could hold onto the hair on her mother's chest and stomach. As she grew bigger, the mother chimpanzee taught her to ride piggyback without falling off when they went through the forest together.

Once when they walked as far as the river, the mother chimpanzee heard a rustling on a big rock close by. A leopard was watching her. The hair on the mother's back stood up the way it always did when she was angry or scared. She turned quickly, and moving as quietly as she could, she hurried back into the forest.

17

By the time the baby was four months old, the mother chimpanzee let the baby's sister groom her very gently and play with her. She tickled the baby and the baby made a soft panting sound as if she were laughing.

The mother chimpanzee never let her little one move very far from her. When the young chimpanzee began to take steps by herself or try to climb a tree, the mother chimpanzee reached to catch her if she lost her balance or fell.

Later, when the little chimpanzee dared to climb high enough, her brother and sister swung her back and forth as she hung from a low branch. The little chimpanzee made funny smiling faces at her brother and sister.

One day, when the spring and the hot summer were over and the winter was coming, the young chimpanzee felt something fall on her nose. She licked it. She had never tasted a raindrop before.

Suddenly the biggest male of the group came down out of a tree and slapped the ground with his hands. He tore off branches and pulled them behind him as he ran down the hill. The other males of the group joined him. They hooted and called because they were excited by the thunder and lightning and the winter rain that was pouring down.

It rained all night long and the young chimpanzee shivered as she lay close to her mother. The next morning she sneezed and coughed. The little chimpanzee had a bad cold. She crept close to her mother as she sat under a tree trying to keep dry.

One day early in the winter, the mother chimpanzee began to look through the forest for termite nests. When she found one, she broke off a little stick. She poked it into the hill made of dirt where the termites laid their eggs and raised their young. The termites hung on to the stick and the mother nibbled them off when she pulled out the stick.

The young chimpanzee did not like termites very much because she still drank milk from her mother.

Sometimes she went off a little way into the forest by herself. Once as she walked under the trees, she saw a face looking down at her. It was a little baboon.

The little baboon and the young chimpanzee played with each other. They climbed into small trees and swung together. They chased each other, calling and hooting, until the mother chimpanzee heard them. She came quickly to get her little one and hurried away with her.

The mother chimpanzee began to feed her young chimpanzee fruits and leaves and nuts. She began to push her away very gently when the young one came to drink milk from her. When her mother first did this the young chimpanzee rolled on the ground, kicking and screaming because she still wanted to drink milk from her mother.

But by the time she was almost four years old the young chimpanzee did not go to her mother for milk anymore. She had learned to hunt for figs and bananas and honey with her brother and sister and the other young chimpanzees.

Sometimes the young chimpanzees walked far away where the ripest figs were growing and sometimes they came to places where baboons were already feeding.

If the strong male chimpanzees were with them, the chimpanzees and the baboons would sometimes fight for the figs.

The big chimpanzees stamped on the ground. They waved branches. They beat their feet against the trees. Then the young chimpanzee crouched down with her arms over her head. If her mother was near, she still ran to cover her young one with her own body.

By the time the young chimpanzee was five years old she had learned to build her own nest every night. She did not sleep with her mother anymore but she still slept in the same tree with her brother and sister and she still liked to sleep in the same tree, close to her mother.

WITHDRAWN

B3
e10
F4

J
599.884
HURD E
MOTHER CHIMPANZEE

C.1

4/3/24
14
2/4/16

14

WITHDRAWN

F1

Manhasset Public Library
Manhasset, New York 11030
Telephone: 627-2300

350